BOOK TWO

A Drop of the Hard Stuff

SIMON & SCHUSTER
YOUNG BOOKS
IN ASSOCIATION WITH CHANNEL FOUR TELEVISION.

Available from all good bookshops.

For further information on the series, write to:
The Marketing Department,
Simon & Schuster Young Books,
Campus 400, Maylands Avenue,
Hemel Hempstead,
Herts HP2 7EZ

Duo Uno Trio

Brenda

Ginger

Davenport

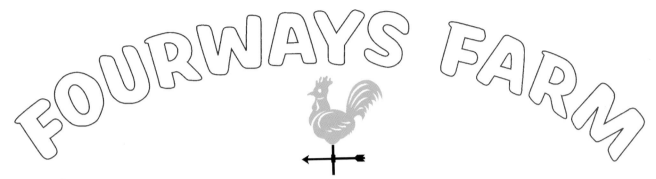

FOURWAYS FARM

A Drop of the Hard Stuff

Dudley   Martha   Godfrey

Text adapted from the scripts of Chris Ellis
based on an original idea by Tom Stanier.

Science Adviser: Malcolm Ward
Science Notes: Sally Nankivell-Aston
Design: Between the Lines
Illustrations: Steve Smallman based on
puppets by Alan Platt and
sets by Max Stewart.

The television programmes on which this work
is based were produced for Channel Four Television
and Nederlandse Onderwijs Televisie
by Case Television Limited.

First published in Great Britain in 1994 by
Simon & Schuster Young Books, Campus 400, Maylands
Avenue, Hemel Hempstead, Herts HP2 7EZ.

British Library Cataloguing in Publications Data available.
ISBN: 0 7500 1647 7

I can see a thing or two from my high perch up above Fourways Farm. There's always something interesting going on down there. Just the other night a chilly wind blew, and what a surprise the animals had when it stopped. There was frost and ice everywhere!

Poor Godfrey got such a whack on the head when he tried to drink from the water trough.

It was worse for Brenda – she was homeless.

"Typical! Look at my home. It's a block of ice – solid, freezing ice. I can't go *in* it, or *on* it! Quack!"

"I say, Brenda, what's going on?" barked Davenport.

"She's going on – on to the ice," said Uno, and he gave Brenda a push. Wheee!

"No! Stop! It's cold! Oh . . .
it's really rather nice," said Brenda.
"Nice?" said Duo. "Rats don't usually
do nice things."

Soon everyone was having fun on the pond.
"I say, this is marvellous!" barked Davenport.
"I hate to admit it," said Godfrey, "but I agree."

"Tell you what, this could be a nice little earner," said Uno. "You're right. Roll up! Only 50p to skate!" yelled Trio.

"Certainly not!" snapped Brenda. "This is my pond and my friends can skate on it free of charge!"

11

Everyone was having too much fun to notice that the day was growing warmer.

"I think I might try a triple loop," said Godfrey. "Tra-la!"

"I say – splendid!" cried Davenport.

Suddenly the ice went C-R-A-C-K!

"Oh dear," groaned Godfrey, up to his middle in freezing cold water. "I knew there had to be a catch."

"Typical!" said Brenda. "I'm getting my pond back, but now there's a stupid great horse in it!"

"We could pull him out with a rope," suggested Trio.

"Well, don't just talk about it," snapped Davenport. "Get a rope!"

"Why did *he* fall through the ice but *we* didn't?" puzzled Davenport.

"Perhaps it's because Godfrey is heavier than any of us?" said Martha.

The rats came back with a strong rope.

"Hold on!" Brenda shouted, and everyone helped to pull Godfrey out of the pond.

Back in the farmyard, the rat pack had thought up another plan to make money out of ice.

"Here, Duo," said Uno. "Fill this bucket with ice and we'll sell cold drinks when the weather warms up."

"Nice one, boss," said Duo.

But Duo put the bucket on the hot stove in the barn.

And in no time at all the ice had turned to water . . . then to steam . . . then to . . . nothing.

In the barn that night the animals talked about the frozen
pond.

"Ice is funny stuff," said Davenport. "It's all gone now."

"I wonder where it went?" said Brenda.
"Maybe it melted back into water?" said Martha.

"That reminds me," said Uno. "Would anyone like an iced drink? For a small price, of course!"

"That would be nice," said Martha.

"Fetch the bucket, Duo," said Uno.

"Er, there's one small problem, boss," said De

"All right then, who's stolen my ice?" cried Uno.

"Dear me," sighed Martha. "Another mystery on H

Farm?"

NOTES FOR PARENTS AND TEACHERS

This book is about the different states of water – as a solid, a liquid and a gas. The story will develop your child's understanding of what happens to water when it is cooled (it changes into ice) and when it is heated (it changes into steam). At the end of the story the ice seems to disappear. This can be used as a starting point for the following activities.

1 Looking closely

Start by talking about when your child has seen ice. Then give him or her an ice-cube to observe and explore. Ask lots of questions to encourage your child to look closely and describe what it feels like. Find out what happens to the ice-cube if you leave it in a warm place.

2 An ice race

Ask your child to place an ice-cube in each of five bowls. Put the bowls in hot, warm and cold places around your home such as: in the fridge, in the freezer, near a radiator, in the airing cupboard, and in the middle of a room – away from a heat source. Look at the cubes every 10 or 15 minutes. Talk about which one(s) melted first and why. Did they all melt? Why/why not?

PS:

You can extend activity 2 by carefully heating an ice-cube in a pan and watching how it changes to water and steam. Then talk about these changes with your child.